BLASTERS

By Fran Pickering
Designed by Gary Cookson
Cover design by Robert Perry

KINGFISHER
An imprint of Larousse plc
Elsley House,
24-30 Great Titchfield Street,
London, W1P 7AD

First published by Larousse plc 1996

4 6 8 10 9 7 5 3

Copyright © Larousse plc and © D. C. Thomson & Co. Ltd 1996.
Factual material and non-character illustration © Larousse plc
1996. Comic character illustration © D. C. Thomson & Co. Ltd
1996. The Beano title and logo is the property of
D. C. Thomson & Co. Ltd.

All rights reserved.
A CIP catalogue record for this book is available from the
British Library

ISBN 0 7534 0076 6

Kingfisher

2

For once Dennis is stumped, but *you* can help him finish his homework. Simply solve the clues and fill in the blanks to make words which either begin or end with DEN.

GNASHER EATING HIS WORDS.

DICTIONARY

DEN TIST Person who looks after your teeth.

Bashed! **DEN TED**

DEN IM What jeans are made from.

Say no. **DEN Y**

OL**DEN** These days were long ago.

Concealed. HID**DEN**

BROA**DEN** Make wider.

4

THE BEANO BRAIN BLASTERS

The Numskulls popped out for a game of football and now they can't find their way back. You can help them out by putting the correct name to each Numskull (look for clues) and then saying where each lives.

RADAR   **BLINKY**   **BRAINY**

CRUNCHER   **SNITCH**

5

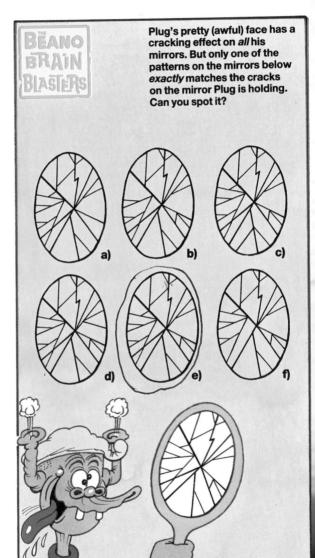

DINOSAURS...
The terrible lizards

About 200 million years ago huge creatures lived on Earth. Their long names were given to them by the people who found their bones and fossils, but what did they call themselves?

land

GNASH! I'LL SHOW YOU TOUGH!

Tyrannosaurus Rex

TYRANNOSAURUS REX

(the tyrant lizard) was a huge meat-eating dinosaur. It could grow up to 14m long and was as tall as six horses piled on top of each other. It had a massive head and its mouth was lined with enormous curved, saw-edged teeth, 15cm long. Like all dinosaurs, Tyrannosaurus had a small brain but this does not mean that it was stupid. But it probably had poor control over

What did T rex eat?

Diplodocus

its movements. There again, would you have been brave enough to tell it so?

DIPLODOCUS

(double-beam) was the longest dinosaur. A skeleton of one found in Utah, USA, was longer than three double-decker buses in a line. But its head was tiny compared to its body – not much bigger than a horse's head. Diplodocus was a vegetarian. All its teeth were at the front of its mouth, so it could reach up into trees and nibble leaves.

IGUANODON

(Iguana-tooth) was a large, two-legged

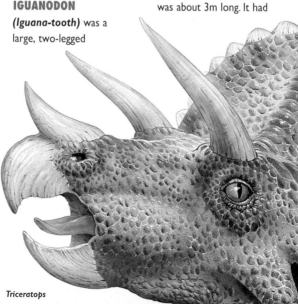

vegetarian, which stood about 5m tall – that's almost as high as a two-storey building. Iguanodon had a sharp, horn-covered bone at the front of its mouth for clipping off tough shoots and leaves and a long tongue to pull the leaves into its mouth.

TRICERATOPS

(three-horned face) was a big-headed dinosaur! Its head was about 3m long. It had

Triceratops

three sharp horns on its head, each one up to 1m long and a bony frill around its neck for defending itself against attack.

I'VE GOT AN ARCHAEO*PTERYX* — AN ANCIENT FATHER!

PTERODACTYLS

(winged finger) were small flying reptiles. They belonged to a family called pterosaurs. They were a Frankenstein mix of 'bits and pieces', with a bird-like beak with teeth, lizard-like legs and backbone, scales like a reptile and clawed fingers.

PTERANODON

(winged toothless) was an enormous flying reptile. Its body was not very big but its wingspan was 7m – wide enough to span a house. Pteranodon was also big-headed. It had a long, toothless beak and a huge crest at the back of its skull.

Pteranodon

ARCHAEOPTERYX

(ancient feather) was about the size of a crow. It is the first known bird, although it was still very like a reptile. It

Which ancient animal had claws on its wings?

had special claws on its wings – just like a modern-day South American bird called

Archaeopteryx   10

the hoatzin. These claws helped Archaeopteryx to climb trees.

Dimorphodon

DIMORPHODON

(two form tooth) was a nightmarish-looking creature. It had a huge, puffin-like head, about 20cm long, that was bigger than its body. It also had

a large tail and wings. Its fingers and toes were very long too!

DINOSAUR EGGS

Dinosaur nests, containing up to 18 eggs, have been found in the Gobi Desert in Mongolia. The eggs had

Which dinosaur stole other dinosaurs' eggs?

hard, 'leathery' shells with a ridged and wrinkled surface. They were more fragile than a bird's egg of today.

Some dinosaurs, including Oviraptor, stole other dinosaurs' eggs and ate them.

Oviraptor had a strong beak with two sharp spikes on the roof of its mouth. It may have used these spikes to crack open the eggs.

DINOSAUR BRAINS

Dinosaurs' brains were housed in a thick bony skull but many were

DINOSAUR

very small. Some were only the size of a nut or an apple. Stegosaurus was over 9m long, but its brain was the size of a walnut.

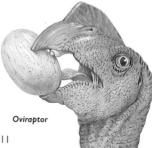
Oviraptor

11

PREHISTORIC PUZZLES

Can you solve these Jurassic brain teasers?

1. "That's odd!" said Roger the Dodger. "These computer keys aren't working properly. When I pressed **A** I got **Z**, when I pressed **B** I got **Y**. The first line of my poem for my natural history homework came out like this:"

RTFZMLWLM RH OLMT TLMV

Can you help him?

2. Dennis had three pet dinosaurs: Triccy, Diccy and Sticcy. The river had overflowed its banks and Dennis had to get his dinosaurs safely to higher ground. They were too stupid to take themselves. The trouble was, unless he was around to keep them apart, Triccy and Sticcy would fight, and Triccy would try to eat Diccy. Diccy and Sticcy are **OK** together. Dennis built a large canoe from a fallen log. It was big enough to take him and one dinosaur. How can Dennis get the dinosaurs to the hill without any of them fighting?

3. Which Dinosaur is the odd one out?

Hamish Steven Warren Charles Duncan Andrew

4. Can you help this dinosaur?

WHICH ROCK DID I USE TO GET RID OF MY TOOTHACHE?

5. Dippy the dinosaur was cleverer than he looked. He almost invented writing – but not quite. He wanted to be famous so he decided to scratch a message on a cave wall. Can you work it out?

DIPLODOCUS WAS HERE

6. Can you give each dinosaur silhouette its correct label?

DIPLODOCUS D

TRICERATOPS B

STEGOSAURUS E

IGUANODON A

TYRANNOSAURUS REX C

14

7. Can you find the names of these reptiles, dinosaurs and prehistoric birds hidden in the word grid?

GECKO, SKINK, RAPTOR,
TURTLE, TORTOISE,
BARYONYX, ALLIGATOR,
PTERANODON,
DIMETRODON,
DIPLODOCUS, LIZARD,
POLACANTHUS,
TRICERATOPS,
KOMODO DRAGON,
ARCHAEOPTERYX,
FRILLED LIZARD,
TYRANNOSAURUS

16

17

The characters listed below have each left something behind. Look closely at the items and say which belongs to which character.

a) BALL BOY
b) MINNIE
c) ROGER
d) GRANNY FROM No 13
e) FATTY
f) LITTLE PLUM
g) OLIVE
h) WALTER

The goodies listed at the bottom of the page are all in Fatty's picnic hamper — and they're hidden in the word square, too. They can read up, down, across, diagonally and backwards or forwards. So get searching!

B	S	P	N	E	K	C	I	H	C
L	I	U	V	W	S	A	C	S	T
U	C	S	T	Q	X	K	J	E	E
R	E	B	C	R	Y	E	Z	I	S
J	C	L	G	U	M	S	I	P	A
E	R	U	C	H	I	P	S	E	N
L	E	N	O	R	E	T	G	E	A
L	A	G	L	U	D	D	S	D	N
Y	M	E	A	S	U	Y	G	C	A
R	E	E	F	F	O	T	L	A	B

BANANAS FUDGE
BISCUITS GUM
CAKES ICE CREAM
CHIPS JELLY
CHICKEN PIES
COLA TOFFEE

21

22

THE BEANO BRAIN BLASTERS

The names of some Beano characters have been mixed up and one letter is missing from each name. Can you work out who they are? When you have done that, you will find that the missing letters make up the name of *another* Beano favourite. Who is it?

NNAY   RTERB

ASHGER

DISYE

MNIEN

FMIFY

HEROES AND VILLAINS
The good, the bad, and the just plain mean

Find out who were the good guys and who were the bad guys in history.

THIS IS THE PLACE FOR A HERO LIKE ME.

heros

Homer

Who was called 'the father of all literature'?

HOMER
(700BC) The Ancient Greeks called Homer 'the father of all

literature'. He wrote the two great adventure poems, *The Iliad* and *The Odyssey*. *The Iliad* describes the Trojan War, while *The Odyssey* tells of the travels of the Greek hero, Odysseus, after he has returned from the fighting.

CONFUCIUS
(551-479BC) Confucius was a Chinese teacher whose sayings and wise advice were collected and published after his death. He was born into a very poor family and most of his ideas

AND A MINX LIKE ME.

Confucius

relate to ways of helping the poor. Some 300 years after his death, his teachings were adopted by the Chinese and his grave became a place to visit.

SMIFFY HE SAYS . . .

WHAT DOES WISE MEAN?

and uncle. There he served Kublai Khan, the Mongol emperor of China, who sent him on many exciting journeys. In 1292 Marco left China. Two years later he arrived home, only to be captured and thrown into prison while fighting for Venice against Genoa. In prison he wrote about his adventures. *The Travels of Marco Polo* is one of the most exciting books ever written.

Who was Marco Polo?

MARCO POLO
(1254–1324) Marco Polo was only 17 when he left Venice to travel to China with his father

Marco Polo

JOAN OF ARC

(1412–1431) Joan was a peasant girl who never learned to read or write, yet she became one of France's best-loved heroines. She lived during the

Joan of Arc

Orléans. She is known as 'The Maid of Orléans'. Joan was betrayed by a group of Frenchmen and captured by the English. She was declared a witch and burned alive at Rouen in 1431.

villains

IVAN THE TERRIBLE

(1530–1584) Ivan was crowned Prince of Russia at the age of three and a half. When he was 12 the first signs

> **SHE'S JUST LIKE ME. I CAN'T READ OR WRITE EITHER.**

time of the Hundred Years' War between France and England. At this time England ruled much of France and the English king, Edward III, claimed to be the heir to the French throne. Joan heard voices in her head, telling her to help the French king, Charles VII. He let her lead the French army and she won a famous victory at

> **Who was the 'Maid of Orléans'**

of his cruelty appeared when he started throwing dogs off the Kremlin battlements to watch them die. When his wife died just before he was 30, Ivan's real reign of terror began. He was responsible for many deaths.

Ivan the Terrible

GULP! THAT THERE GUY MAKES ME SEEM *SOFT!*

WANTED

GENGHIS KHAN

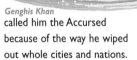

Genghis Khan

Ivan the Terrible had his own private army. They were called the Oprichniki. They dressed in black, rode black horses and their emblem was a dog and a broom.

called him the Accursed because of the way he wiped out whole cities and nations.

GENGHIS KHAN

(1167-1227) At the age of 13, Genghis Khan became chief of a Mongol tribe. He chose his own name, which means Very Mighty King. He conquered lands stretching from Russia to China and the Pacific Ocean. The Persians

NED KELLY

(1855-1880) Ned Kelly was the son of an Irish convict. He became Australia's most famous outlaw. Kelly began his

Who was Australia's most famous outlaw?

Ned Kelly

life of crime in his mid-teens, stealing horses and cattle. He hated the police and the Kelly Gang became known as robbers and murderers who would shoot any policemen who got in their way. In 1880, Kelly's plan to derail a trainload of policemen and then kill them, failed and he was caught and hanged.

27

HEROES AND VILLIANS

Can you solve these fearsome brain teasers?

I. Can you find the names of these 'BADDIES' from well-known stories hidden in the word square?
SCAR, SHREDDER, CAPTAIN HOOK, JAFAR, BILL SYKES, CRUELLA DEVILLE, JOKER, SHERE KHAN, MING THE MERCILESS, SHERIFF OF NOTTINGHAM, WICKED WITCH OF THE WEST.

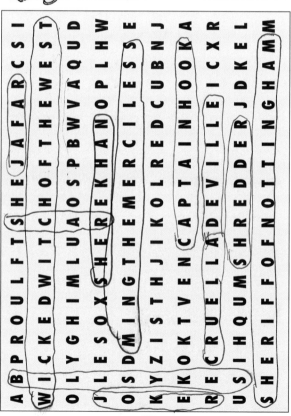

2. Marco Polo went to the Great Wall of China. But someone got there before him and wrote something on it. What does it say?

WELCOME TO CHINA

3. Can you rearrange these jumbled words (anagrams) to form the name of a well-known hero or villian?

Thread mill pave	
Lend kyle	
The clad live	
Cradling gear	
I all base	
Duck in trip	
She hang king	
Leaf by zither	

33

MYTHS AND LEGENDS
The art of story-telling

Long, long ago, not just before we had TV and films and computers, but before we had books, story-telling was very important. If people weren't sure about something, they made up a story to explain it anyway. Some of these stories are still told today.

myths

RA THE SUN GOD

In Ancient Egypt, Ra was one of the most important gods. The Egyptians believed that Ra was the creator of all gods and all men and each pharaoh was known as 'Son of Ra'. The Egyptians believed in the power of the Sun. They explained its rising and setting by saying that each day Ra

> **Who was the laughing Buddha?**

> LOVELY SPELL OF WEATHER WE'RE HAVING!

sailed across the top of the world in a boat, bringing sunlight. At night he sailed beneath the world and the Sun disappeared. Ra was always shown as a man with a falcon's head and a solar disc for a crown.

Ra the Sun God

Ho-Tei

the world on a treasure ship. The ship contains magic objects that give them power.

SARASVATI

Hindus have three gods. One of them, Brahma, is the creator god. When he created the first woman, Sarasvati, he fell in love with her. He grew three more faces so that he could always see her. Sarasvati, is the Hindu goddess of

HO-TEI

Ho-tei is a god of happiness – one of the seven Shinto

Who invented the Sanskrit alphabet?

wisdom, music, knowledge and the Arts. She became the wife of Brahma. Sarasvati is said to have invented Sanskrit which is the language of the Hindus. She is usually pictured riding a white swan and playing on an instrument called a vina.

gods of good fortune. His nickname is 'the laughing Buddha' and he is usually pictured as a plump, bald, cheerful little man, often carrying a sack full of precious things. He and his companions are thought to sail around

Sarasvati

The story of Brunhild is one of heroic feats, royal revenge, and magical powers. Odin was the Norse god who created the world. He was the god of wisdom, war, art, culture and the dead. His special helpers were the Valkyries, super-

who would die. Brunhild was the leader of the Valkyries. She was beautiful and very strong. She vowed she would never love a man unless he was stronger than herself. When she disobeyed Odin and spared the lives of Siegmund and

EAT YOUR HEARTS OUT, VALKYRIES.
HERE COME THE BEANO
SUPER WOMEN!

Sieglinde, the parents of the hero Siegfried, Odin punished her by putting her to sleep, surrounded by a ring of fire. Siegfried rode through the fire to rescue her. Later, Brunhild was tricked into believing that Siegfried had deserted her. Out of anger, she married someone else but later Brunhild discovered that she had been deceived and had Siegfried murdered. She threw herself on his funeral pyre.

Who were the Valkyries?

women who flew over battlefields, choosing who would become heroes and

THESEUS

Theseus was the son of Aegeus, king of Athens. But when his story grew into a legend, people claimed that his real father was Poseidon, god of the sea. Theseus was told that Greece was poor because of the huge taxes that were paid to king Minos, the powerful ruler of Crete. Each year, 14 young Athenians were sent to Crete to be sacrificed to a beast called the Minotaur. The beast was half-man and half-bull and ate human flesh. The Minotaur lived in an underground maze of tunnels called the Labyrinth, from which there was no escape.

Who lived in a maze of underground tunnels?

Theseus went to Crete as part of the sacrifice and, by using his wits as well as his strength, killed the Minotaur. He found his way out of the maze by following the thread from a ball of string.

OI, YOU! I'M THE ONLY BONY OLD HAG IN THE BEANO!

BABA YAGA

Baba Yaga was a skinny, bony old witch in Eastern European legend. She lived in a hut in the forest. Her nickname was 'Bonylegs'. She had power over all animals, but did not treat them well.

MYTHICAL PUZZLES

Can you solve these mythical brain teasers?

1. Baba Yaga's animals have run away and are hiding in the forest. There's one behind each tree. Can you rearrange the letters to see who is behind each tree?

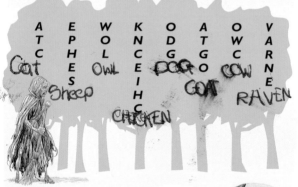

A	E	W	K	O	A	O	V
T	P	O	N	D	T	W	A
C	H	L	C	G	G	C	R
	E		E		O		N
	S		I				E
			H				
			C				

Handwritten answers: Cat, Sheep, Owl, Dog, Goat, Cow, Raven, Chicken

2. Can you solve this riddle?

My first is in stars and also in sun
My second's a cuppa when the work's done.
My third is in always and also in aye,
My fourth is in tint but never in dye.
My fifth is in under and upper and out,
My last is in smile but not in a pout.
My whole is a model, big or quite small,
To put in your garden, your temple or hall.

3. Theseus killed the Minotaur, but he forgot his ball of string and has lost his way out of the labyrinth. Can you help him find it?

4. Les Pretend, the famous explorer, has discovered the doorway to a secret room in the pyramid. It has a picture of Ra, the Sun god on it. Before he can reach the room he has to cross a patterned floor. This floor is cleverly booby-trapped. The only way across follows a logical path from the starting square. Can you work it out?

Help Walter to finish his jigsaw by figuring out which of the pieces at the bottom *exactly* fits the missing shape.

THE BEANO BRAIN BLASTERS

Does Sidney have a secret admirer? Solve the riddle to discover who sent this mystery birthday card.

My first is in starry and also in night,
My second in cloudy but never in bright.
My third is a letter you'll find if you look
At Beano and comic and cover and book!
My next is in aircraft but never in fly,
My last is in swallow, high up in the sky.
My whole is the person who sent this to Sid,
And here is a clue — I'm a pretty cool kid.

To Sidney
Happy Birthday
Love from
?

THE BEANO BRAIN BLASTERS

Beat Billy to the middle of this word wheel by solving all the clues. Each word begins with the last letter of the previous word and, to start you off, we've given you the very first letter.

1. The 'nosy' Numskull.
2. Teacher's boss.
3. The Menace.
4. Football is Ball Boy's favourite.
5. What Rasher has instead of a foot.
6. Number one's listening pal.
7. The Dodger.
8. Colour of Vic Volcano's hair.
9. What Gnasher and Gnipper are.

Okay, how many words can you make from jumbling up the letters of Minnie's name?

THE BEANO BRAIN BLASTERS

MINNIE THE MINX

THE BEANO BRAIN BLASTERS

ANSWERS

PAGE 4

Dentist; Dented; Denim; Deny; Olden; Hidden; Broaden.

PAGE 5

a) Brainy, Brain Dept; b) Cruncher, Mouth Dept; c) Snitch, Nose Dept; d) Blinky, Eye Dept; e) Radar, Ear Dept.

PAGE 6

Look closely at the letter pyramid. If you start from the middle of the bottom line and move upwards, you will find the word LADDER. That would have helped Les reach the top of the mountain.

PAGE 7
Plug is holding the mirror e).

PAGE 12
1. The letters of the alphabet have been put back to front. The poem reads:

IGUANODON IS LONG GONE

2. Diccy and Sticcy are okay together so Dennis leaves them and takes Triccy. He then goes back for Sticcy, takes him to the hill and brings back Triccy. Dennis leaves Triccy behind while he takes Diccy, who can then be left safely with Sticcy. Dennis then returns to fetch Triccy.

PAGE 13
3. The answer is CHARLES because his name has seven letters while all the others have only six.

4. The dinosaur used rock B.

5. Dippy's message read **DIPLODOCUS WAS HERE**

PAGE 14
6. DIPLODOCUS = **D**, TRICERATOPS = **B**, STEGOSAURUS = **E**, IGUANODON = **A**, TYRANNOSAURUS REX = **C**

PAGE 15
7. YOUR GRID SHOULD LOOK LIKE THIS:

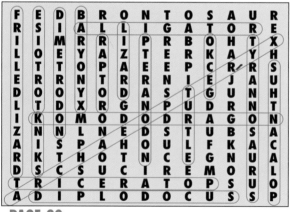

PAGE 20
a) Ball Boy's boots and football; b) Minnie's hat; c) Roger's Book of Dodges; d) Granny from No. 13 has left her hat; e) Fatty's lunch box; f) Little Plum's arrow; g) Olive's stewpot; h) Walter's flowers.

PAGE 21

The goodies in the grid should look like this.

PAGE 22

c) is the tunnel which leads to Gnasher's bones.

PAGE 23

The names are Danny; Erbert; Gnasher; Sidney; Minnie and Smiffy.

The missing letters make up the name Dennis.

PAGE 28

1. YOUR GRID SHOULD LOOK LIKE THIS:

```
A B P R O U L F T S H E J A F A R C S I
W I C K E D W I T C H O F T H E W E S T
O L Y G H I M L U A O S P B W V A Q U D
J L E S O X S H E R E K H A N O P L H W
O S D M I N G T H E M E R C I L E S S E
K Y Z I S T H J I K O L R E D C U B N J
E K O K T V E N C A P T A I N H O O K A
R E C R U E L L A D E V I L L E I C X R
U S I H Q U M S H R E D D E R J D K E L
S H E R I F F O F N O T T I N G H A M M
```

PAGE 29

2. The wall says:

WELCOME TO CHINA

3. Vlad The Impaler; Ned Kelly; Edith Cavell; Grace Darling; Isabella; Dick Turpin; Genghis Khan; Elizabeth Fry.

PAGE 38

1. Cat; Sheep; Owl; Chicken; Dog; Goat; Cow; Raven.

PAGE 38 cont

1. The answer is **STATUE**

PAGE 39

3. The maze answer is like this. Follow the red string to freedom.

4. The inner colour becomes the outer colour of the correct square in the next row.

PAGE 40

b) is the correct jigsaw piece.

PAGE 41

Ivy's presents are as follows:

Pink box, trainers; green box, chocolates; blue box, kite; red box, skipping rope; yellow box, skateboard.

PAGE 42

Sid's card is from his twin sister, Toots.

PAGE 43

1. Snitch; 2. Head; 3. Dennis; 4. Sport; 5. Trotter; 6. Radar; 7. Roger; 8. Red; 9. Dogs.

PAGE 44

There are **SEVEN** catapults.

PAGE 45

Tin, Mix, Tie, Hit, Ten, Then, Mine, Thin, Teen, Next, Meet, Hint, Exit, Mite, Time, Mint, Them, Thine, Theme, Metre and lots lots more. Award yourself a prize if you find more than us.